Y0-AGH-924

GO FLY A KITE, CHARLIE BROWN

Books by Charles M. Schulz

Peanuts®
More Peanuts®
Good Grief, More Peanuts®!
Good Ol' Charlie Brown
Snoopy
You're Out of Your Mind, Charlie Brown!
But We Love You, Charlie Brown
Peanuts® Revisited
Go Fly a Kite, Charlie Brown
Peanuts® Every Sunday
It's a Dog's Life, Charlie Brown
You Can't Win, Charlie Brown
Snoopy, Come Home
You Can Do It, Charlie Brown
We're Right Behind You, Charlie Brown
As You Like It, Charlie Brown
Sunday's Fun Day, Charlie Brown
You Need Help, Charlie Brown
Snoopy and The Red Baron
The Unsinkable Charlie Brown
You'll Flip, Charlie Brown
You're Something Else, Charlie Brown

GO FLY A KITE, CHARLIE BROWN

A NEW PEANUTS® BOOK

by Charles M. Schulz

HOLT, RINEHART AND WINSTON
New York • Chicago • San Francisco

Published, August, 1960
Twelfth Printing, January, 1968

Published simultaneously in Canada by
Holt, Rinehart and Winston of Canada, Limited

Copyright © 1959, 1960 by United Feature Syndicate, Inc.
Printed in the United States of America
All rights reserved

8299505

Library of Congress Catalog Card Number 60-5911

SO HERE I AM STARTING A NEW YEAR..

BUT AM I ANY DIFFERENT?
NOPE! I'M THE SAME OL' DOG!

DAY AFTER DAY AND YEAR AFTER YEAR... NEVER A CHANGE!
SNOOPY

SOMETIMES I MARVEL AT MY CONSISTENCY!
SCHULZ

HOW'S THE BIRDHOUSE COMING ALONG, CHARLIE BROWN?

WELL, I'M A LOUSY CARPENTER, I CAN'T NAIL STRAIGHT, I CAN'T SAW STRAIGHT AND I ALWAYS SPLIT THE WOOD...

I'M NERVOUS, I LACK CONFIDENCE, I'M STUPID, I HAVE POOR TASTE AND ABSOLUTELY NO SENSE OF DESIGN..

SO, ALL THINGS CONSIDERED, IT'S COMING ALONG OKAY!
SCHULZ

WELL, SCHROEDER, WHAT HAPPENED TO YOU?

I WAS LISTENING TO BEETHOVEN'S THIRD SYMPHONY... IN THE SECOND MOVEMENT THERE'S A BEAUTIFUL PASSAGE... JUST BEAUTIFUL...

WHENEVER I HEAR IT, I GET COLD CHILLS...

SO I CAUGHT COLD!
SCHULZ

LOOK OUT!!

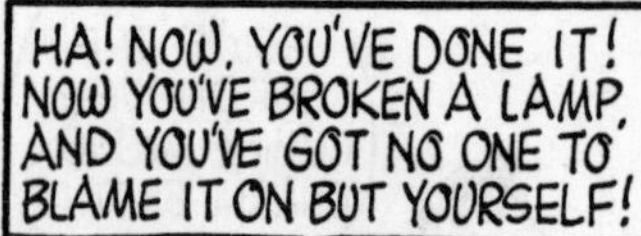
HA! NOW, YOU'VE DONE IT! NOW YOU'VE BROKEN A LAMP, AND YOU'VE GOT NO ONE TO BLAME IT ON BUT YOURSELF!

MAYBE I COULD BLAME IT ON SOCIETY!
SCHULZ

FOR ME THIS BLANKET PROVIDES ALL THE SECURITY OF A GOOD INSURANCE PROGRAM

DID YOU NOTICE THAT I CUT A LITTLE PIECE OUT OF YOUR BLANKET, LINUS? I HAD TO MAKE A QUILT FOR MY DOLL'S BED... I HOPE YOU WON'T MIND...

GOOD GRIEF!

YOU JUST PUT A HOLE IN MY ANNUITY!
SCHULZ

I THINK IT'S TIME TO GO HOME AND TAKE A SHOWER..

GOING TO GET ALL CLEANED UP, EH, "PIG-PEN"?

WELL, I'VE LEARNED NEVER TO EXPECT TOO MUCH FROM A SHOWER...

I HAVE TO BE SATISFIED IF IT JUST SETTLES THE DUST!
SCHULZ

WHEN I GROW UP, I'M GOING TO BE A COUNTRY DOCTOR..

HA! I CAN JUST SEE YOU LIVING IN THE COUNTRY!

I DIDN'T SAY I'D LIVE IN THE COUNTRY...

I'LL COMMUTE FROM THE CITY IN MY SPORTS CAR!
SCHULZ

WHEN I GET BIG, I'M GOING TO BE A HUMBLE LITTLE COUNTRY DOCTOR

I'LL LIVE IN THE CITY SEE, AND EVERY MORNING I'LL GET UP, CLIMB INTO MY SPORTS CAR AND ZOOM INTO THE COUNTRY!

THEN I'LL START HEALING PEOPLE...I'LL HEAL EVERYBODY FOR MILES AROUND!

I'LL BE A WORLD FAMOUS HUMBLE LITTLE COUNTRY DOCTOR!
SCHULZ

I HAD TO GET A SHOT TODAY

DID YOU? GEE, I HATE TO GET SHOTS!

WHEN I'M A DOCTOR MYSELF, THOUGH, IT'LL BE DIFFERENT.

FOR THE FIRST TIME IN MY LIFE I'LL BE ON THE RIGHT SIDE OF THE OL' NEEDLE!
SCHULZ

YOU A DOCTOR! HA! THAT'S A BIG LAUGH!

YOU COULD NEVER BE A DOCTOR! YOU KNOW WHY?

BECAUSE YOU DON'T LOVE MANKIND, THAT'S WHY!

I LOVE MANKIND... IT'S PEOPLE I CAN'T STAND!!
SCHULZ

I ADMIRE YOUR AMBITION TO BE A DOCTOR, LINUS...

OF COURSE, EIGHT YEARS IS A LONG TIME TO STUDY, BUT THEN..
EIGHT YEARS?

GOOD GRIEF!

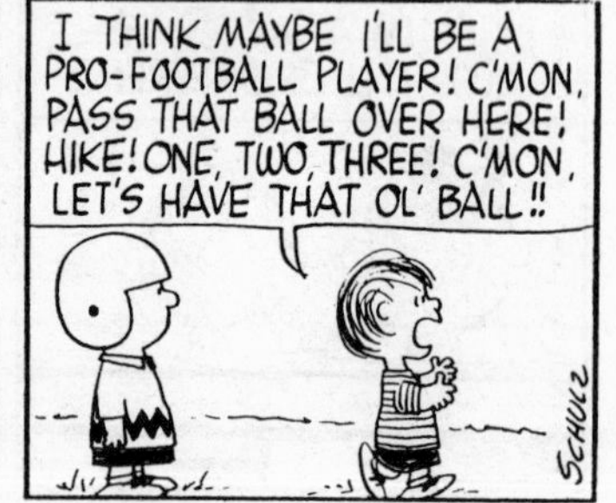
I THINK MAYBE I'LL BE A PRO-FOOTBALL PLAYER! C'MON, PASS THAT BALL OVER HERE! HIKE! ONE, TWO, THREE! C'MON, LET'S HAVE THAT OL' BALL!!
SCHULZ

WELL, WHAT ARE YOU DOING HERE?

GO ON HOME! WE DON'T WANT YOU AROUND HERE! WHO ASKED YOU TO COME BY IN THE FIRST PLACE? NOBODY! GO ON HOME!

YOU KNOW, IT'S A STRANGE THING ABOUT CHARLIE BROWN... YOU ALMOST NEVER SEE HIM LAUGH!
SCHULZ

SOMETIMES WHEN I GET UP IN THE MORNING, I FEEL VERY PECULIAR..

I FEEL LIKE I'VE JUST GOT TO BITE A CAT! I FEEL LIKE IF I DON'T BITE A CAT BEFORE SUNDOWN, I'LL GO CRAZY!!

BUT THEN I JUST TAKE A DEEP BREATH AND FORGET ABOUT IT..

THAT'S WHAT IS KNOWN AS REAL MATURITY!
SCHULZ

CHARLIE BROWN WHAT WOULD BE YOUR REACTION IF SOMEONE SAID YOU COULD HAVE YOUR LIFE OVER AGAIN?

YOU MEAN EXACTLY AS I'VE LIVED IT? NO CHANGES? EVERYTHING HAPPENING JUST THE WAY IT DID BEFORE?

UH HUH...WHAT WOULD BE YOUR REACTION?

AAAUGHH!
SCHULZ

HERE SNOOPY! I'LL THROW THE BALL, AND YOU CHASE IT! OKAY? C'MON, BOY! HERE, SNOOPY!

GOOD GRIEF! IF THERE'S ANYTHING I **DON'T** FEEL LIKE DOING, IT'S CHASING A **BALL**!

IT'S HARD TO HIDE BEHIND SOMEONE WHO'S VERTICAL WHEN YOU'RE HORIZONTAL!
SCHULZ

!

CLOMP!

PTUI!

HOW DEFT CAN YOU GET?
SCHULZ

WHAM!

SCHULZ

IN THE OLDEN DAYS THIS WAS KNOWN AS BRINGING THE WARRIOR HOME ON HIS SHIELD!

ONCE YOU'VE GOT A KITE IN THE AIR, CHARLIE BROWN, IS IT ANY TROUBLE GETTING IT DOWN AGAIN?

WHAM!

THAT'S ONE PROBLEM I'VE NEVER HAD TO WORRY ABOUT
SCHULZ

SCHULZ

ISN'T THE SKY A BEAUTIFUL BLUE TODAY, LINUS?

LOOK THERE...DID YOU EVER SEE ANYTHING NICER?

SCHULZ

THIS IS MY LITTLE TOY FARM..

I'LL PUT THE BARN OVER HERE, AND I'LL PUT THE HOUSE HERE...

THEN I GUESS I'LL PUT THIS LITTLE TREE RIGHT HERE..

SCHULZ

YOU STUPID KITE! I'LL STOMP YOU!

I'LL MANGLE YOU!

I'LL KICK YOU!!

IT'S FLYING!
SCHULZ

I DON'T FEEL WELL..

MY HEAD HURTS, AND EVERY TIME I MOVE IT, I GET DIZZY...

I JUST DON'T FEEL WELL...

SICKEST GUN IN THE WEST!
SCHULZ

A DOG'S LIFE IS A LONELY LIFE..

CATS HATE US...HORSES STEP ON US...WILD ANIMALS DESPISE US...

SIGH

THANK GOODNESS FOR **PEOPLE** !
SCHULZ

HE'S GREAT, I TELL YOU... REALLY GREAT!

REMEMBER HOW HE USED TO SWAT THE OL' HORSEHIDE LAST SUMMER?

WELL, YOU HAVEN'T SEEN ANYTHING UNTIL YOU'VE SEEN HIM KICK THAT PIGSKIN!

WHY CAN'T THEY JUST PLAY THEIR OL' GAMES, AND LEAVE THE ANIMALS OUT OF IT?
SCHULZ

I OWE YOU AN APOLOGY "PIG-PEN".. I'VE BEEN TEASING YOU A LOT LATELY..

BUT WHO AM **I** TO TEASE **YOU**? YOU MAY BE DIRTY, BUT AT LEAST YOU HAVE CHARACTER!

ME? I'M **BLAH**! THAT'S JUST WHAT I AM..**BLAH!** I'M COMPLETELY **BLAH**! I WAS BORN **BLAH**, AND I'LL DIE **BLAH**!

WHEN YOU'RE LOOKING AT **ME**, YOU'RE LOOKING AT THE ALL-TIME NUMBER-ONE CHAMPION **BLAH**!!
SCHULZ

ARE YOU AND LINUS STILL FIGHTING?
NO, I HAVE A PHILOSOPHY THAT PREVENTS THAT SORT OF THING

I HAVE A PROFOUND PHILOSOPHY THAT HAS STOOD THE TEST OF TIME DIFFICULT AS IT MAY BE FOR THE LAYMAN TO UNDERSTAND..

I HAVE A PHILOSOPHY THAT HAS BEEN REFINED IN THE FIRES OF HARDSHIP AND STRUGGLE...

"LIVE AND LET LIVE!"
SCHULZ

I CAN'T THINK OF THAT WORD...

THERE'S ONE CERTAIN WORD THAT DESCRIBES YOUR PERSONALITY, CHARLIE BROWN, BUT I JUST CAN'T THINK OF WHAT IT IS...

"BLAH"?

THAT'S IT!
SCHULZ

LOOK, YOU DON'T HAVE TO TELL **ME** I'M BLAH!

I **KNOW** I'M **BLAH**!
WELL, THEN THERE'S STILL HOPE FOR YOU CHARLIE BROWN...

IF YOU RECOGNIZE THIS IN YOURSELF THEN THAT'S THE FIRST STEP UP FROM BLAHDOM!

"**BLAHDOM**"?
SCHULZ

HOW CAN ANYONE EVER LIKE SOMEONE AS BLAH AS I AM?!
PLEASE DON'T DESPAIR, CHARLIE BROWN..

MAYBE THERE'S A GIRL SOMEWHERE IN THE WORLD WHO IS JUST AS BLAH AS YOU... MAYBE YOU'LL MARRY HER..

AND MAYBE YOU'LL RAISE A WHOLE FLOCK OF BLAH KIDS, AND THEN MAYBE THEY'LL GO OUT AND MARRY SOME OTHER BLAH KIDS, AND..

AAUGH!
SCHULZ

BEETHOVEN USED TO BE FOND OF TAKING LONG WALKS IN THE COUNTRY...

HE WAS ALWAYS INSPIRED BY THE BEAUTIFUL SOUNDS OF THE COUNTRYSIDE...

YOU BLOCKHEAD, COME BACK HERE WITH THAT BALL!!

BEETHOVEN HAD IT NICE!
SCHULZ

?
SNIF
SNIF
SNIF
?

AH, HA! I **THOUGHT** I SMELLED PIZZA!

MMMMMM

SIGH I COULD EAT A TWENTY-FOUR INCH PIZZA WITHOUT BATTING A LIP!
SCHULZ

THESE ROCKS ARE A RELEASE FOR MY PENT-UP EMOTIONS.

WHEN I FEEL ALL TIED UP INSIDE, I JUST STAND HERE AND THROW ROCKS INTO THAT VACANT LOT!

HELLO, CHARLIE BROWN YOU BLOCKHEAD!

SOMETIMES I THINK I'M KIND OF A VACANT LOT MYSELF...
8-17
SCHULZ

YOU THINK THIS IS AN ORDINARY PILE OF ROCKS, DON'T YOU? WELL, IT **ISN'T**!

THESE ROCKS ARE MEANT TO BE THROWN IN ANGER! WHEN I GET REAL MAD, I THROW ROCKS AS HARD AS I CAN!!

IT JUST SO HAPPENS THAT TODAY I FEEL PRETTY GOOD
SCHULZ

THESE ROCKS ARE ESPECIALLY GROOMED TO BE HURLED IN ANGER!

AFTER YOU'VE THROWN ALL OF THEM, DO YOU GO OUT AND PICK THEM UP?

OH, YES...I KEEP USING THE SAME ROCKS OVER AND OVER..

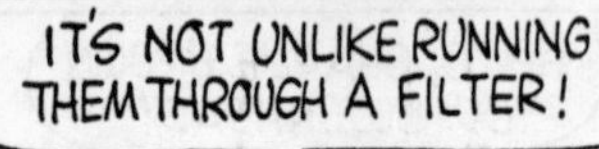
IT'S NOT UNLIKE RUNNING THEM THROUGH A FILTER!

SCHULZ

THIS IS FOR ALL THE NASTY THINGS THEY SAID ABOUT GEORGE WASHINGTON!

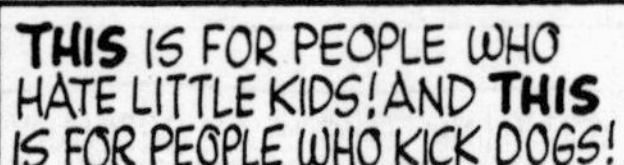
THIS IS FOR PEOPLE WHO HATE LITTLE KIDS! AND THIS IS FOR PEOPLE WHO KICK DOGS!

THIS IS FOR HOT SUMMER NIGHTS! AND THIS IS FOR COLD WINTER MORNINGS! AND THIS IS FOR LIES AND BROKEN PROMISES!

DO YOU HAVE ANY REQUESTS?
SCHULZ

THIS IS FOR PEOPLE WHO DON'T LIKE THE MAYOR! THIS IS FOR PEOPLE WHO DON'T LIKE THE GOVERNOR!

THIS IS FOR PEOPLE WHO DON'T LIKE BEETHOVEN!

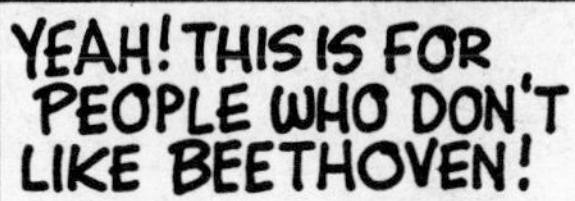
YEAH! THIS IS FOR PEOPLE WHO DON'T LIKE BEETHOVEN!

SCHULZ

I'VE DECIDED THAT THROWING ROCKS IS NO SOLUTION..

A PERSON JUST HAS TO LEARN TO DEVELOP SELF-CONTROL...

ONLY AN IDIOT COULD BE CONVINCED THAT THROWING ROCKS INTO A VACANT LOT WILL SOLVE HIS PROBLEMS!

SCHULZ

DID IT EVER OCCUR TO YOU THAT "PIG-PEN" MIGHT BE CARRYING THE DIRT AND DUST OF SOME PAST CIVILIZATION?

NOTICE HOW THE DUST CLINGS TO HIM...

HE COULD HAVE ON HIM SOME OF THE SOIL OF ANCIENT BABYLON

SORT OF MAKES YOU WANT TO TREAT ME WITH MORE RESPECT, DOESN'T IT?
SCHULZ

JUST THINK OF IT.. THE DIRT AND DUST OF FAR-OFF LANDS BLOWING OVER HERE AND SETTLING ON "PIG-PEN"!

IT STAGGERS THE IMAGINATION! HE MAY BE CARRYING SOIL THAT WAS TROD UPON BY SOLOMON OR NEBUCHADNEZZAR OR GENGHIS KHAN!
!

THAT'S TRUE, ISN'T IT?

SUDDENLY I FEEL LIKE ROYALTY!
SCHULZ

POOR OL "PIG-PEN"

THEY SAY HE CARRIES ON HIM THE DIRT AND DUST OF ANCIENT CIVILIZATIONS...

HISTORY IS PASSING BEFORE MY EYES!
SCHULZ

I SEE WHERE THE PRICE OF HAIRCUTS MAY GO UP AGAIN..

MY DAD SAYS HE'S GOING TO BUY A PAIR OF CLIPPERS, AND CUT **MY** HAIR HIMSELF...

I HOPE HE CUTS YOUR EARS OFF!

I KEEP FORGETTING THAT CHARLIE BROWN'S DAD IS A BARBER!
SCHULZ

DID ANYONE EVER TELL YOU THAT YOU HAVE PRETTY EYES, SCHROEDER?

MUSICIANS GET UNNERVED WHEN YOU TELL THEM THAT THEY HAVE PRETTY EYES
SCHULZ

THEY'RE ALWAYS WRITING ABOUT EVIL STEP-MOTHERS!

EVERY STEP-MOTHER IN THESE FAIRY TALES IS DESCRIBED AS BEING EVIL!

DO YOU KNOW WHAT THIS AMOUNTS TO?
WHAT?

A BLANKET CONDEMNATION OF STEP-MOTHERS!
SCHULZ

SNOWFLAKES FASCINATE ME... MILLIONS OF THEM FALLING GENTLY TO THE GROUND..

AND THEY SAY THAT NO TWO OF THEM ARE ALIKE!

EACH ONE COMPLETELY DIFFERENT FROM ALL THE OTHERS....

THE LAST OF THE RUGGED INDIVIDUALISTS!
SCHULZ

SAY, I DO! I DO!! I DO!!!

NOPE, I GUESS I DON'T...

..IT'S JUST A LITTLE DIRT..
?

FOR ONE BRIEF, EXCITING MOMENT I THOUGHT I NEEDED A SHAVE!
SCHULZ

ALL RIGHT! SO IT'S SUPPERTIME!

I **KNOW** IT'S SUPPERTIME! I'LL BE WITH YOU AS SOON AS THIS PROGRAM IS OVER!

NOW JUST SIT STILL AND ENJOY THE SHOW...

SIGH
SCHULZ

CHARLIE BROWN, WE NEED YOUR ADVICE...

SAY A PERSON HAS A BAG OF CANDY, AND HALF OF THE PIECES HAVE COCONUT IN THEM.. SAY THE PERSON SHE IS GOING TO SHARE THEM WITH CAN'T STAND COCONUT..

DOES HE HAVE TO ACCEPT THE COCONUT ONES ALONG WITH THE OTHERS IF HE THINKS SHE IS TRYING TO GET RID OF THEM BECAUSE SHE DOESN'T LIKE THEM EITHER?

I HAVE NEVER PRETENDED TO BE ABLE TO SOLVE MORAL ISSUES!
SCHULZ

CHARLIE BROWN, DO YOU THINK THAT SANTA CLAUS REALLY KNOWS HIS JOB?

OH, YES... AFTER ALL, HE'S BEEN AT IT FOR A LONG TIME..

THAT'S JUST WHAT HAS ME WORRIED...

PERHAPS IT'S TIME FOR A **YOUNGER** MAN TO TAKE OVER!
SCHULZ

THIS ROCKET BUSINESS IS FASCINATING

EVERY DAY THEY SEEM TO COME UP WITH SOMETHING NEW

FOR AWHILE THEY WERE SENDING UP DOGS... NOW THEY'RE SENDING UP MICE..

THAT'S A VERY HEALTHY TREND!
SCHULZ

I'M GOING TO BE STAYING AT MY GRAMMA'S HOUSE FOR A FEW NIGHTS..
C.B.

HOW COME, CHARLIE BROWN?
BECAUSE MY MOTHER WENT TO THE HOSPITAL LAST NIGHT..
C.B.

MY DAD SAID SHE'LL BE ALL RIGHT...IN FACT, HE SAID SHE'LL BE HOME IN ABOUT FIVE DAYS..

FIVE DAYS? I WONDER... DO YOU SUPPOSE... I WONDER IF...NO, IT COULDN'T BE... STILL...
SCHULZ

A BABY SISTER?

I'M A FATHER!

I MEAN MY DAD'S A FATHER! I'M A BROTHER! I HAVE A BABY SISTER!! I'M A BROTHER!

YOU DIDN'T ACT LIKE THAT WHEN I WAS BORN!
SCHULZ

SO CHARLIE BROWN HAD A BABY SISTER LAST NIGHT!

BOY, THERE SURE WAS A LOT OF EXCITEMENT AROUND HERE ABOUT MIDNIGHT...PEOPLE RUNNING IN ALL DIRECTIONS...

..CARS COMING AND GOING.. TELEPHONES RINGING...THINGS STILL HAVEN'T CALMED DOWN..

SCHULZ
AND IN ALL THE EXCITEMENT, NOBODY HAS REMEMBERED TO FEED THE DOG!

SO YOU HAVE A NEW BABY SISTER, HUH, CHARLIE BROWN?

YES, AND I'M SO HAPPY...

HAPPY?

I SUPPOSE IT'S NEVER OCCURRED TO YOU THAT OVER-POPULATION IS A SERIOUS PROBLEM?!
SCHULZ

I GUESS CHARLIE BROWN'S NEW BABY SISTER CAME HOME TODAY..

I'D KIND OF LIKE TO GO IN, AND SEE HER...

STILL, MAYBE I'D BETTER NOT...

I'D JUST AS SOON WAIT FOR A FEW DAYS UNTIL HER EYES ARE OPEN!
SNOOPY
SCHULZ

HEY, C'MON!

CHARLIE BROWN HAD A BABY SISTER! HE'S HANDING OUT CHOCOLATE CIGARS!

CONGRATULATIONS, CHARLIE BROWN!
THANK YOU, 'PIG-PEN'..

NOT BAD...THIS SHOULD HAPPEN MORE OFTEN!
SCHULZ

YOU'RE ALWAYS AFTER PEOPLE TO MAKE NEW YEAR'S RESOLUTIONS!

WHY DO WE HAVE TO MAKE OUR RESOLUTIONS RIGHT ON JANUARY FIRST? WHAT'S WRONG WITH MAY SIXTEENTH OR SEPTEMBER TWENTY-THIRD?

WHY JANUARY FIRST?

IT'S **NEATER**!
SCHULZ

WHEN I GET BIG, I WANT TO BE A GREAT PHILANTHROPIST!

YOU HAVE TO HAVE A LOT OF MONEY TO BE A GREAT PHILANTHROPIST..

I WANT TO BE A GREAT PHILANTHROPIST WITH SOMEONE ELSE'S MONEY!
SCHULZ

ITS NO WONDER SOME PEOPLE GET FAT!

ALL THEY EVER DO IS EAT! ALL THEY EVER **THINK** ABOUT IS EATING!

SNOOPY

SCHULZ
YOU CAN SAY THAT AGAIN!

DO YOU EVER THINK MUCH ABOUT THE FUTURE, LINUS?

OH, YES... ALL THE TIME

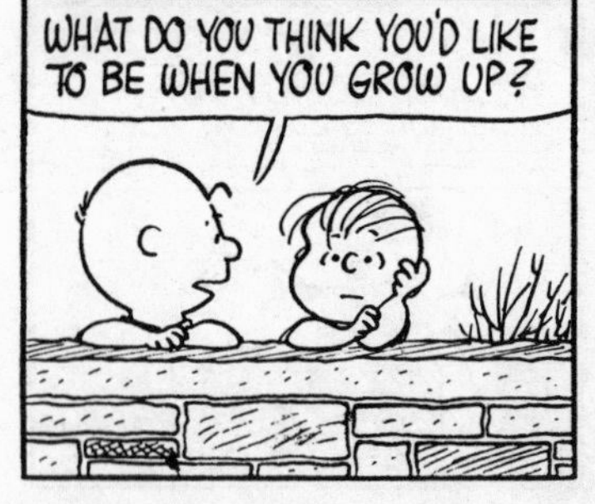
WHAT DO YOU THINK YOU'D LIKE TO BE WHEN YOU GROW UP?

OUTRAGEOUSLY HAPPY!
SCHULZ

SO CHARLIE BROWN FINALLY GOT A BABY SISTER

GEE, WE NEVER GET ANY NEW BABIES AT **OUR** HOUSE

OURS EITHER..WE HAVEN'T HAD ANY NEW BABIES FOR A **LONG** TIME..

ALL **WE'VE** GOT IS THIS HERE **OLD** BABY!
SCHULZ

HAVE THEY DECIDED ON A NAME FOR YOUR SISTER YET, CHARLIE BROWN?

YES, HER NAME IS GOING TO BE SALLY!
SALLY?

SALLY... SALLY BROWN... GOOD OL' SALLY BROWN!

IT FIGURES.!
SCHULZ

WAS YOUR BABY SISTER BORN AT ACE HOSPITAL, CHARLIE BROWN?

NO, I DON'T THINK SO... WHY?

THAT'S TOO BAD..

IF SHE HAD BEEN BORN AT ACE HOSPITAL, SHE WOULD HAVE RECEIVED ALL NINE BEETHOVEN SYMPHONIES FREE!
SCHULZ

WELL, CHARLIE BROWN..HAVE YOU FELT ANY JEALOUSY SO FAR TOWARD YOUR NEW BABY SISTER?
OH, NO.. SHE'S A REAL DECENT SORT

YOU MEAN YOU HAVEN'T FELT EVEN THE LEAST BIT JEALOUS?
NO, NOT EVEN THE LEAST BIT..

YOU DRIVE ME CRAZY!
SCHULZ

I DON'T THINK IT'S RIGHT TO BRING NEW BABIES INTO THIS UNCERTAIN WORLD...THIS IS THE WRONG TIME!

WHAT ARE YOU GONNA DO WITH ALL THOSE BABIES WHO ARE LINED UP WAITING TO BE BORN?

YOU JUST CAN'T TELL THEM TO GO AWAY AND **WAIT** FOR ANOTHER THOUSAND YEARS, CAN YOU? **CAN YOU**?
NO, I GUESS YOU CAN'T..

THE WHOLE TROUBLE WITH YOU IS YOU NEVER THINK THESE THINGS THROUGH!
SCHULZ

YOU KNOW, SNOOPY..HAVING A BABY SISTER IS KIND OF NICE...

I DON'T THINK I'LL FEEL SO ALONE ANY MORE..

WELL, I HOPE HE'S RIGHT, BUT I WOULDN'T KNOW...I NEVER HAD ANY SISTERS OR BROTHERS

I WAS AN ONLY DOG!
SCHULZ

SO THEY DECIDED TO NAME YOUR SISTER SALLY DID THEY?

WELL, SALLY IS A CUTE NAME, I GUESS..

IT MAKES YOU THINK OF A GIRL WHO IS SWEET AND GENTLE AND PRETTY AND MAYBE JUST A LITTLE BIT SHY...

...LIKE THE NAME LUCY!
SCHULZ

Hey, Violet!

WAIT UNTIL YOU SEE THE PAIR OF SLEEPERS I BOUGHT FOR LITTLE SALLY..

YOU CERTAINLY ARE A DEVOTED BROTHER, CHARLIE BROWN
WELL, I'M TRYING TO BE

SCHULZ

STUPID DOG!

THE WHOLE WORLD COULD GET BLOWN UP ANY MINUTE AND ALL **YOU** THINK OF IS **DANCING**!!

I **COULD** THINK OF **EATING**, BUT IT'S TOO EARLY IN THE DAY!
SCHULZ

THE TROUBLE WITH **YOU** IS YOU DON'T SHOW ENOUGH **RESPECT**

IF IT WEREN'T FOR HUMANS, YOU DOGS WOULDN'T EVEN **BE** HERE!

FROM NOW ON I WANT RESPECT!!

SCHULZ

HERE, TAKE IT...DON'T BE SO SUSPICIOUS!

WHAT A DOG!
CHOMP CHOMP

HE'S GETTING SO HE DOESN'T TRUST ANYBODY

HE'D MAKE A GOOD HUMAN BEING!
SCHULZ

CHARLIE BROWN, YOUR HAVING A BABY SISTER HAS SET ME TO THINKING..

FIRST YOU SEE A YOUNG COUPLE LIVING IN THIS HOUSE ALL ALONE...

THEN ALONG COMES A BABY... THEN ANOTHER ONE...AND THEN ANOTHER ONE...PRETTY SOON THE HOUSE IS FULL OF LITTLE KIDS!

I KNOW WHAT YOU MEAN... THEY SEEM TO HAVE A WAY OF ACCUMULATING LIKE OLD MAGAZINES!
SCHULZ

..AND FIVE IS TWENTY-TWO..

NINETEEN HUNDRED AND FIFTY NINE PLUS TWENTY-TWO IS NINETEEN HUNDRED AND EIGHTY-ONE
?

WHEN I'M TWENTY-TWO AND SALLY IS SEVENTEEN, DO YOU THINK SHE'LL GO OUT WITH ME?

THIS HAVING A BABY SISTER MAY DO A LOT FOR CHARLIE BROWN..

IT'S JUST LIABLE TO MAKE HIM INTO A NEW PERSON!

THAT'S A FRIGHTENING THOUGHT...

I CAN THINK OF NOTHING IN ALL THIS WORLD MORE OBNOXIOUS THAN A WELL-ADJUSTED CHARLIE BROWN!
SCHULZ

YOU THINK HAVING A BABY SISTER IS GREAT, DON'T YOU?

FROM NOW ON YOU'RE GOING TO HAVE TO SHARE THE AFFECTION OF YOUR MOTHER AND DAD! BUT YOU THINK YOU WON'T MIND THAT, DON'T YOU?

YOU THINK IT'LL BE FIFTY-FIFTY, DON'T YOU? WELL, IT WON'T! WITH A BABY SISTER, IT'LL BE FIFTY ONE-FORTY NINE! MAYBE EVEN SIXTY-FORTY!!

I'LL BET YOU DIDN'T REALIZE THAT FAMILY LIFE WAS SO MATHEMATICAL!
SCHULZ

YOU'RE SO SWEET, SNOOPY..I WISH I COULD GIVE YOU A BIG KISS, BUT OF COURSE, I CAN'T...

SCHULZ
THE CURSE OF A FUZZY FACE!

LET'S START THE LETTER THIS WAY..."DEAR SANTA, WE HOPE YOU HAD A NICE SUMMER"...

WHAT DO YOU MEAN, "A NICE SUMMER"?
YOU KNOW... HIS VACATION... EVEN SANTA CLAUS HAS TO HAVE A VACATION..

I IMAGINE HE GOES OFF SOME PLACE TO REST, OR PLAY GOLF OR DO SOME SKIN DIVING... DON'T YOU THINK SO?

FOR SOME REASON I JUST CAN'T PICTURE SANTA CLAUS SKIN DIVING!
SCHULZ

YOU KNOW, IN A WAY, "DEAR SANTA CLAUS" IS RATHER STUFFY..

PERHAPS SOMETHING A LITTLE MORE INTIMATE WOULD BE BETTER...SOMETHING JUST A SHADE MORE FRIENDLY...

HOW ABOUT, "DEAR FATTY"?
SCHULZ

YOU'RE REALLY LUCKY, CHARLIE BROWN...

ALL MY LIFE I WANTED A BABY SISTER... BUT WHAT DID I GET? I GOT **THIS** STUPID THING!

DEFINE, "STUPID THING."
SCHULZ

I'VE JUST COME TO REALIZE SOMETHING..

I NEVER KNEW IT BEFORE, BUT LUCY REALLY RESENTS MY HAVING BEEN BORN..SHE'S WANTED A SISTER LIKE YOU HAVE!

WELL, IT'S LIKE MY AUNT MARIAN ALWAYS SAYS, YOU CAN CHOOSE YOUR FRIENDS, BUT YOU CAN'T CHOOSE YOUR RELATIVES

YOUR AUNT MARIAN IS WONDERFULLY WISE!
SCHULZ

SO NOW IT COMES OUT! YOU'VE ALWAYS WANTED A SISTER, NOT A BROTHER!

I HAVE HALF A NOTION TO LEAVE HOME..
WELL, WHY DON'T YOU? AND TAKE THIS STUPID BLANKET OF YOURS WITH YOU!

ARE YOU TRYING TO GET RID OF ME?!
SCHULZ

IT'S TOO MUCH FOR ME TO TAKE.. I CAN'T STAND IT!

IT'S PRETTY DISHEARTENING TO FIND OUT THAT YOUR OWN SISTER WISHES YOU HAD NEVER BEEN BORN..

"NEVER BEEN BORN"... GOOD GRIEF! DO YOU KNOW WHAT THAT MEANS? JUST STOP TO THINK ABOUT IT...

WHY, THE THEOLOGICAL IMPLICATIONS ALONE ARE STAGGERING!
SCHULZ

I'M RUNNING AWAY FROM HOME, VIOLET!
OH? I KNOW A GOOD JOKE ABOUT A LITTLE BOY RUNNING AWAY FROM HOME..

THIS MAN CAME ACROSS THIS LITTLE BOY STANDING BY THE CURB, SEE, AND HE ASKED HIM WHAT HE WAS DOING...

THE LITTLE BOY SAID, "I'M RUNNING AWAY FROM HOME, BUT I'M NOT ALLOWED TO CROSS THE STREET!"

THAT'S A RIOT!
SCHULZ

I'M SORRY IF I'VE UPSET YOU, LINUS..

OH, THAT'S ALL RIGHT.. *SNIF*
NO, I MEAN IT.. AFTER ALL, YOU **ARE** MY BROTHER

WE'RE PART OF THE SAME FAMILY... BROTHER AND SISTER...BLOOD RELATIVES...

NO MATTER HOW YOU LOOK AT IT, I'M **STUCK** WITH YOU!
SCHULZ

SNOOPY, DID YOU SEE LINUS GO BY HERE?

I'LL TICKLE YOU 'TIL YOU TELL ME! TICKLE TICKLE TICKLE TICKLE!
HEE HEE HEE HEE HEE HEE

HE WENT THAT WAY, HUH? GOOD! YOU'RE LUCKY YOU TOLD ME!

I'D MAKE A LOUSY SPY!
SCHULZ

I THOUGHT HAVING A BABY SISTER WOULD CHANGE MY WHOLE LIFE, BUT IT HASN'T..

PEOPLE STILL HATE ME..NOBODY REALLY LIKES ME...I GET JUST AS DEPRESSED AS I ALWAYS DID..

POOR CHARLIE BROWN..

OF ALL THE CHARLIE BROWNS IN THIS WORLD, HE'S THE CHARLIE BROWNEST!
SCHULZ

DO YOU EVER WORRY ABOUT THE WORLD GETTING BLOWN UP CHARLIE BROWN?

IT ALL DEPENDS... WHAT DAY IS TODAY?

TUESDAY
WELL, ON TUESDAYS I WORRY ABOUT PERSONALITY PROBLEMS...

THURSDAY IS MY DAY FOR WORRYING ABOUT THE WORLD GETTING BLOWN UP!
SCHULZ

I'M JUST AMAZED BY THE WONDER OF IT ALL..

FIRST MY DAD BUYS A BARBER SHOP, THEN HE GETS MARRIED, THEN I'M BORN AND NOW SALLY IS BORN..

OUR FAMILY IS REALLY GROWING...

I CAN SEE THE NEW SIGN IN MY DAD'S SHOP NOW.... "HAIRCUTS-TEN DOLLARS"
SCHULZ

I'VE NEVER BEEN SO MAD IN ALL MY LIFE!

I WENT DOWN TO THE STORE TO GET A HALLOWEEN MASK AND THEY WERE ALL OUT OF THEM!

AREN'T THEY GOING TO ORDER ANY MORE?
HA! ARE YOU KIDDING?

THEY WERE BUSY PUTTING UP CHRISTMAS DECORATIONS!
SCHULZ

Z

Z

Z Z Z Z Z Z Z Z Z Z Z Z Z Z
SCHULZ

LOOK IT'S A PICTURE OF SALLY, CHARLIE BROWN'S NEW BABY SISTER..

OH ISN'T SHE CUTE?
SHE'S REAL CUTE
THAT'S SUCH A CUTE PICTURE

SHE SURE IS CUTE, CHARLIE BROWN
SHE'S REAL CUTE
YES SHE'S REAL CUTE

IF THEY EVER TOOK "CUTE" OUT OF THE ENGLISH LANGUAGE, WE'D ALL PERISH!
SCHULZ

YOU THINK YOUR SALLY IS CUTE..YOU SHOULD SEE **HIM**!

HIM? "HIM" WHO?

OH, GOOD GRIEF!
SCHULZ

THAT'S NOT A REAL BABY! THAT'S JUST A DOG DRESSED UP LIKE A BABY!

GOO!
SCHULZ

WHAT WAS THAT?
WHAT WAS WHAT?

I THOUGHT I HEARD SOMETHING OUT BY THE FRONT DOOR..

CHARLIE BROWN HAS HAD TOO MUCH ON HIS MIND LATELY...HE'S CRACKING UP!

ANYONE CARE FOR A FUZZY BABY?
SCHULZ

LOOK, THIS IS YOUR BABY, NOT MINE! I HAVE MY OWN BABY SISTER AT HOME!

YOU WERE THE ONE WHO PUT THE BONNET ON HIM... NOW YOU TAKE CARE OF HIM!

I'M NOT INTERESTED ANY MORE.. I HAVE OTHER THINGS TO DO!

YOU'RE A POOR EXCUSE FOR A MOTHER!!
MAMA!
SCHULZ

HERE, SNOOPY, LET ME TAKE THAT STUPID BONNET OFF YOUR HEAD..

THERE!

BOY, I'M GLAD THAT SILLY BUSINESS IS OVER..

I WASN'T SURE WHETHER I WAS GOING TO END UP IN AN ORPHANAGE OR AT THE HUMANE SOCIETY!
SNOOPY
SCHULZ

I'VE NEVER FELT SO DEPRESSED BEFORE...

WELL, I WISH I KNEW WHAT TO SAY, CHARLIE BROWN, BUT YOU'RE A HARD PERSON TO HELP...

YOU MEAN I HAVE A PERSONALITY SO COMPLICATED THAT IT DEFIES ANALYSIS?

NO, I MEAN YOU HAVE A PERSONALITY SO **SIMPLE** THAT IT DEFIES ANALYSIS!
SCHULZ

HAVING A BABY SISTER HAS MADE A DIFFERENT PERSON OUT OF ME..

YOU JUST THINK IT HAS, CHARLIE BROWN...YOU SEE, YOU'RE A "STATUS SEEKER"...

YOU JUST WANT SOMETHING THAT WILL BUILD YOU UP IN THE EYES OF THE OTHER KIDS IN THE NEIGHBORHOOD..

YOU COULD HAVE ACCOMPLISHED THE SAME THING WITH AN AUTOGRAPHED BASEBALL!
SCHULZ

BOY! WHEN I SIT UP HERE, I CAN SEE FOR MILES!
SNOOPY

I CAN SEE THE ENTIRE CONTINENT!

I CAN SEE THE WHOLE **WORLD**!

I CAN SEE CLEAR OVER TO THE NEXT YARD!
SCHULZ

DID YOU KNOW THAT CRICKETS CHIRP BY RUBBING PARTS OF THEIR FORE-WINGS TOGETHER?

NO, I'VE ALWAYS THOUGHT THEY USED THEIR HIND LEGS..

A POPULAR MISCONCEPTION!
SCHULZ

ALL RIGHT, SO SHE SHOULDN'T HAVE HUNG IT OUTSIDE WHEN IT WAS SO COLD!

YOU'RE LUCKY MOM EVEN WASHES YOUR BLANKET!

HOW WAS SHE TO KNOW IT WOULD FREEZE?!

SCHULZ

DO YOU REALIZE THAT WE STILL HAVEN'T SEEN SALLY, CHARLIE BROWN?

YES, TELL US WHAT SHE LOOKS LIKE
WELL, SHE'S SORT OF...

NOT THE **POSITIVE** DETAILS.. THE **NEGATIVE** DETAILS...

YES, JUST TELL US THAT SHE DOESN'T LOOK LIKE **YOU**!
SCHULZ

I THINK I KNOW WHAT YOUR TROUBLE IS, CHARLIE BROWN..

NOW THAT ALL THE THRILL AND EXCITEMENT OF YOUR BABY SISTER BEING BORN IS OVER, YOU'RE HAVING AN **EMOTIONAL LETDOWN**..

DID **YOU** HAVE AN EMOTIONAL LETDOWN AFTER LINUS WAS BORN?

I DIDN'T GET A CHANCE.. JUST **SEEING** HIM WAS A LETDOWN!
SCHULZ

SO WHAT WOULD BE SO TERRIBLE IF MY OWN BABY SISTER LOOKED LIKE **ME**?

YOU DON'T UNDERSTAND, CHARLIE BROWN..

LOOKS AREN'T IMPORTANT TO A BOY...

BUT A GIRL **MUST** HAVE A PRETTY FACE!
SCHULZ

LISTEN TO THIS, CHARLIE BROWN...

IT SAYS HERE THAT THERE ARE OVER SIX HUNDRED AND SEVENTY THOUSAND DIFFERENT KINDS OF INSECTS!

WOW!

TAKE COMFORT, LITTLE FELLOW.. YOU ARE NOT ALONE!
SCHULZ

I'M INTERESTED IN LEARNING HOW TO DEVELOP A REAL CONCERN FOR OTHERS..

YOU MEAN YOU WANT TO BE CONCERNED ABOUT THOSE WHO ARE LESS FORTUNATE THAN YOU?

NO, I WANT TO BE CONCERNED ABOUT THOSE WHO ARE **MORE** FORTUNATE THAN I AM..

I WANT TO BRING THEM DOWN TO MY LEVEL!
SCHULZ

SOMETIMES I LISTEN TO MY BABY SISTER CRYING AT NIGHT, AND IT TEARS MY HEART OUT!

THE WORLD IS FILLED WITH TROUBLE, AND SHE'S SO INNOCENT
INNOCENT? SHE'S JUST **HUNGRY**, CHARLIE BROWN!

THAT MAKES ME FEEL EVEN WORSE..

THE WORLD IS IN TURMOIL, AND MY BABY SISTER IS STARVING TO DEATH!
OH, GOOD GRIEF
SCHULZ

EVERY DAY THE PAPERS ARE FULL OF HORRIBLE THINGS!

I HATE TO SEE LITTLE SALLY GROW UP IN SUCH A WORLD!

DON'T LOOK SO MUCH ON THE DARK SIDE, CHARLIE BROWN... LOOK ON THE BRIGHT SIDE.. THINK OF THE ADVANCEMENTS...

..BY THE TIME SHE GROWS UP, THERE'LL BE THREE MAJOR LEAGUES!
SCHULZ

IT'S ALL RIGHT FOR YOU TO BE COMPLACENT, LINUS...

YOU DON'T HAVE A BABY SISTER TO WORRY ABOUT! I TELL YOU THE WORLD IS GETTING WORSE ALL THE TIME!

MURDERS, ROBBERIES, AUTOMOBILE ACCIDENTS, BLACKMAIL, ALL SORTS OF TERRIBLE THINGS!

DON'T FORGET ABOUT KICKING DOGS...PEOPLE ARE ALWAYS KICKING DOGS, TOO..
SCHULZ

I THINK THE WORLD IS MUCH BETTER TODAY THAN IT WAS, SAY, FIVE YEARS AGO..

HOW CAN YOU SAY THAT? DON'T YOU EVER READ THE PAPERS? DON'T YOU EVER LISTEN TO THE RADIO?

HOW CAN YOU STAND THERE, AND TELL ME THIS IS A BETTER WORLD?

I'M IN IT NOW!
SCHULZ

SO YOU THINK THE WORLD IS GETTING BETTER?

WELL, IF YOU'VE GOT SO MUCH CONFIDENCE IN THE WORLD'S GETTING BETTER, HOW COME YOU HANG ON TO THAT BLANKET?

TOUCHÉ!
SCHULZ

WHAT ARE YOU TWO STANDING HERE LOOKING SO WORRIED ABOUT?

WE'RE AFRAID OF THE FUTURE!

ARE YOU WORRIED ABOUT ANYTHING IN PARTICULAR?
OH, NO... WE'RE WORRIED ABOUT EVERYTHING!

YES, OUR WORRYING IS VERY BROADMINDED!
SCHULZ

I ENVY YOU, SNOOPY...YOU DON'T HAVE TO WORRY ABOUT ANYTHING!

YOU DON'T HAVE TO WORRY ABOUT THE FUTURE OF THE WORLD OR ABOUT INFLATION OR ABOUT ANYTHING!!

SCHULZ
I WONDER WHERE MY NEXT MEAL IS COMING FROM!

IT'S FANTASTIC!

I'M PERFECTLY CLEAN NOW, BUT JUST LET ME STEP OUT OF THE HOUSE FOR ONE MINUTE...

WHAM!

YOU KNOW WHAT I AM? I'M A DUST MAGNET!
SCHULZ

BOY, IT'S TOUGH TO BE A DOG WHEN IT RAINS!

OF COURSE, I'M LUCKIER THAN A LOT OF DOGS.... AT LEAST I HAVE A DOG HOUSE TO GO HOME TO...

SCHULZ

MOM'S GOING DOWNTOWN, LINUS... DO YOU WANT HER TO GET YOU ANYTHING?

TELL HER I NEED A NEW COWBOY HAT...
WHAT SIZE?

MEDIOCRE!
SCHULZ

SNOOPY, HAVE YOU EVER FELT THAT YOU WERE A BORE?

HAVE YOU EVER FELT THAT PEOPLE WERE BORED BY EVERYTHING YOU SAID?

HAVE YOU EVER FELT THAT THEY WEREN'T THE LEAST BIT INTERESTED IN ANYTHING YOU..

SCHULZ
Z

CATCH THE SNOWFLAKES ON YOUR TONGUE, LUCY!

IT'S TOO EARLY... I NEVER EAT JANUARY SNOWFLAKES...I ALWAYS WAIT UNTIL FEBRUARY...

SCHULZ
THEY SURE LOOK RIPE TO ME!

I'M THE KIND OF PERSON WHO IS KIND OF HARD TO GET TO KNOW, I GUESS..

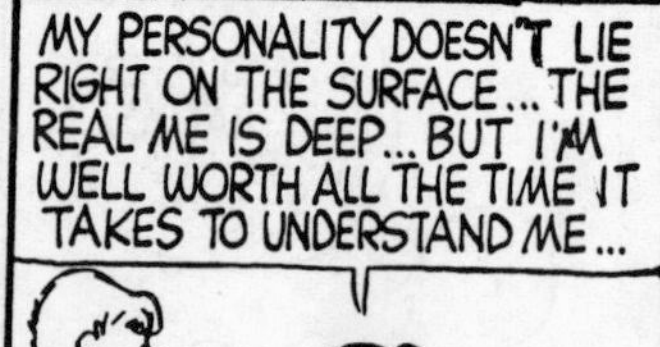
MY PERSONALITY DOESN'T LIE RIGHT ON THE SURFACE... THE REAL ME IS DEEP... BUT I'M WELL WORTH ALL THE TIME IT TAKES TO UNDERSTAND ME...

IN OTHER WORDS, TO KNOW ME, IS TO LOVE ME!

SCHULZ
SIGH

I GUESS I LET TOO MANY THINGS BOTHER ME...

I SEEM TO GET UPSET BY ANY LITTLE THING I HEAR

I THINK I'M GOING TO HAVE TO ERECT SORT OF A MENTAL FENCE TO KEEP UNPLEASANT NEWS OUT OF MY MIND...

DON'T MAKE IT A PICKET FENCE... THEY'RE AWFULLY HARD TO PAINT!
SCHULZ

MY GRAMMA IS STAYING WITH US FOR A FEW DAYS...

LAST NIGHT WE ALL WENT TO THE SHOW EXCEPT GRAMMA.. SHE DOESN'T LIKE SHOWS...

SO SHE STAYED HOME ALONE THEN, HUH?

NO, WE GOT A GRAMMA-SITTER!
SCHULZ

HERE'S THE FAITHFUL DOG FOLLOWING THE KIDS TO SCHOOL..

HERE'S THE FAITHFUL DOG SITTING DOWN OUTSIDE WHILE ALL THE KIDS GO INSIDE..

HERE'S THE FAITHFUL DOG LYING DOWN OUTSIDE WAITING FOR SCHOOL TO LET OUT...

HERE'S THE FAITHFUL DOG SUDDENLY REALIZING HE'S WASTING HIS TIME!
SCHULZ

I HEAR YOU KIND OF LIKE YOUR NEW TEACHER, LINUS...

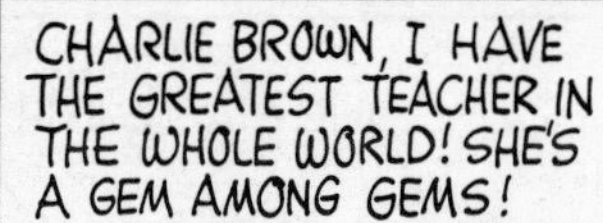
CHARLIE BROWN, I HAVE THE GREATEST TEACHER IN THE WHOLE WORLD! SHE'S A GEM AMONG GEMS!

SIGH

I NEVER REALIZED THAT THE NATIONAL EDUCATION ASSOCIATION TURNED OUT SUCH A FINE PRODUCT!

SCHULZ

WHAT'S THIS ABOUT YOU AND A "MISS OTHMAR"? WHO IN THE WORLD IS MISS OTHMAR?

SHE'S MY TEACHER...SHE UNDERSTANDS ME!

EITHER SHE'S A GENIUS, OR SHE'S NEW ON THE JOB
SCHULZ

I THINK MISS CTHMAR LIKES ME..

THIS MORNING SHE WAS CALLING THE ROLL...SHE SAID, "DAVID, BETTY, CRAIG, WILLIAM, TONY, MARY, TOMMY, CYNTHIA..."

..AND THEN SHE SAID, "LINUS..." THAT'S JUST THE WAY SHE SAID IT..."LINUS".....SHE CAME RIGHT OUT, AND SAID MY NAME JUST AS PLAIN AS DAY...

I THINK MISS OTHMAR REALLY LIKES ME!
SCHULZ

YOU ALWAYS **OVERDO** THINGS!

IT'S ALL RIGHT TO **LIKE** A TEACHER, BUT IT'S WRONG TO **WORSHIP** HER!

I NEVER SAID I **WORSHIP** HER...

I JUST SAID THAT I'M VERY FOND OF THE GROUND ON WHICH SHE WALKS!
SCHULZ

YOU SAY MISS OTHMAR IS ONLY HUMAN...WELL, I SAY SHE'S MORE!

LIKE ALL GOOD TEACHERS, SHE HAS IN HER BEING A TOUCH OF THE SPIRIT FIRED BY THE DEDICATION OF HER CALLING!

SNIF

FORGIVE ME FOR CRYING, BUT THAT'S ONE OF THE MOST MOVING SPEECHES I'VE EVER HEARD...
SCHULZ

?
OH, MISS OTHMAR! WHY, MISS OTHMAR!

DON'T EVEN SAY THINGS LIKE THAT, MISS OTHMAR...WHY, MISS OTHMAR!

I CAN'T STAND IT! I JUST CAN'T STAND IT!
SCHULZ

I FEEL SORRY FOR LITTLE BABIES..

WHEN A LITTLE BABY IS BORN INTO THIS COLD WORLD, HE'S CONFUSED! HE'S FRIGHTENED!

HE NEEDS SOMETHING TO CHEER HIM UP...

THE WAY I SEE IT AS SOON AS A BABY IS BORN, HE SHOULD BE ISSUED A BANJO!
SCHULZ

SOMETIMES I LIE AWAKE AT NIGHT WONDERING WHY I WAS BORN..

WHY WAS I PUT ON THIS EARTH? WHAT AM I DOING HERE?

..AND THEN SUDDENLY IT HITS ME..

I HAVEN'T GOT THE SLIGHTEST IDEA!
SCHULZ

DO YOU WANT TO HEAR SOMETHING CUTE THAT MY LITTLE SISTER DID YESTERDAY?

OFFHAND, CHARLIE BROWN, I CAN THINK OF NOTHING THAT WOULD BORE ME MORE!

DON'T WORRY, I'M NOT EVEN GOING TO **TRY** TO TELL **YOU**!!
SCHULZ

HOW'S SALLY, CHARLIE BROWN?

SHE'S FINE THANK YOU..

I'M GLAD YOU MENTIONED HER BECAUSE SHE DID SOME-THING KIND OF CUTE YESTERDAY, AND I'D LIKE TO TELL..

SCHULZ

VIOLET, WOULD YOU CARE TO HEAR SOMETHING CUTE THAT SALLY DID YESTERDAY?

SALLY IS MY LITTLE BABY SISTER, YOU KNOW...

MY NAME IS CHARLIE BROWN!
SCHULZ

SCHROEDER, WOULD YOU LIKE TO HEAR SOMETHING CUTE THAT SALLY DID YESTERDAY?

SURE...I'D BE GLAD TO...
WELL, IT WAS LIKE THIS... SHE WAS..

SCHULZ

LINUS! SUPPERTIME! MOTHER SAYS COME RIGHT IN..

OKAY, I'LL BE THERE AS SOON AS I FINISH THIS ROAD...
STOP

MOTHER SAYS TO COME IN RIGHT NOW, AND SHE MEANS RIGHT NOW!

SIGH
YOU CAN'T FIGHT CITY HALL!
SCHULZ

I CAN NEVER GO ANYPLACE WITH ANOTHER PERSON BECAUSE THAT PERSON USUALLY DOESN'T LIKE ME...

IF I'M WITH TWO OTHER PEOPLE, I ALWAYS FEEL THAT THEY'RE TALKING ABOUT ME WHENEVER I HAPPEN TO TURN MY BACK...

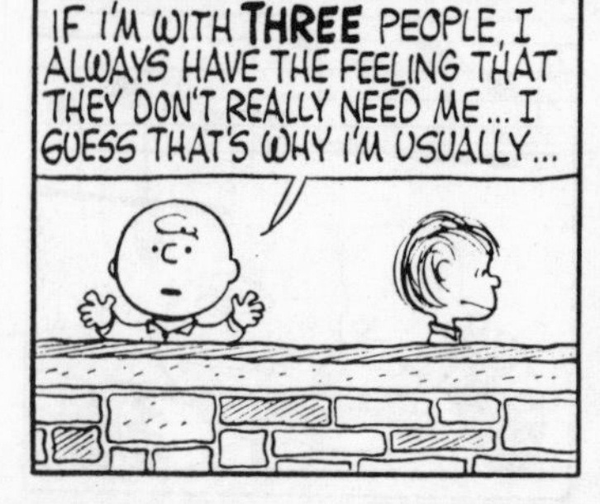
IF I'M WITH THREE PEOPLE, I ALWAYS HAVE THE FEELING THAT THEY DON'T REALLY NEED ME... I GUESS THAT'S WHY I'M USUALLY...

..ALONE!
SCHULZ

I'M INCLINED TO AGREE WITH YOU, CHARLIE BROWN..

BUT ON THE OTHER HAND WE MUST BE CAUTIOUS IN OUR THINKING...

WE MUST BE CAREFUL NOT TO "THROW OUT THE BABY WITH THE BATH"

PLEASE PARDON THE EXPRESSION
SCHULZ

BLAUGH!

CHLORINE!
SCHULZ

YOU'RE WEAK, YOU'RE HOMELY, YOU'RE STUPID, YOU'RE...

NOW, WAIT A MINUTE! IT'S ONLY EIGHT O'CLOCK IN THE MORNING...YOU'RE STARTING IN ON ME KIND OF EARLY, AREN'T YOU?

I CAN'T HELP IT, CHARLIE BROWN...

YOU HAVE SO MANY FAULTS IT TAKES A WHOLE DAY TO LIST THEM!
SCHULZ

HI, "PIG-PEN"... YOU LOOK PRETTY CLEAN TODAY FOR A CHANGE
WELL, IT'S A PROBLEM, CHARLIE BROWN..

I'M CLEAN NOW, BUT I DON'T KNOW HOW LONG IT WILL LAST..

!

YOU CAN SEE WHAT I'M UP AGAINST!
SCHULZ

BOY, IF I WERE A LEAF, I WOULDN'T BE SO ANXIOUS TO LEAVE HOME..

I'D STICK TO THAT OL' TREE JUST AS LONG AS I COULD!

SEE, SMARTY? WHAT DID IT GET YOU?
SCHULZ

I THINK LEAVES ARE CRAZY!

THEY ALL SEEM SO ANXIOUS TO FALL OFF THE TREE LIKE SOMEONE WHO CAN HARDLY WAIT TO GET AWAY FROM HOME

BOY, IF I WERE A LEAF, THEY'D NEVER GET ME OUT OF THE TREE! I'D WHIMPER AND WHINE AND BEG FOR MERCY...

I'D PROBABLY EMBARRASS THE WHOLE TREE!
SCHULZ

WELL! THE FIRST FALLING LEAF OF THE SEASON...

THE FIRST LEAF TO MAKE THE COURAGEOUS LEAP! THE FIRST LEAF TO DEPART FROM HOME! THE FIRST LEAF TO PLUNGE INTO THE UNKNOWN!

THE FIRST LEAF TO DIE!!
SCHULZ

HI LEAF!
SCHULZ

IF I WERE A LEAF, YOU'D NEVER CATCH **ME** FALLING OFF A TREE!

I'D HANG ON FOR DEAR LIFE! I'D STAY WITH THAT TREE UNTIL THEY CAME TO GET ME!

EVEN THEN THEY'D HAVE TO DRAG ME OFF! I'D KICK AND SCREAM, AND PUT UP A REAL FIGHT!

I'D MAKE A LOUSY LEAF!
SCHULZ

WELL! I'M GLAD TO SEE THERE'S **ONE** SMART LEAF IN THE CROWD!

I'M GLAD TO SEE THAT SOMEONE HAS SENSE ENOUGH TO STAY PUT!

!

SIGH
SCHULZ

SCHULZ

WOW!

WHATS THE MATTER? IS IT SNOWING?

BOY, I'LL SAY IT'S SNOWING!

IT'S PITCH WHITE OUTSIDE!
SCHULZ

SNOOPY! SUPPERTIME!

ALL RIGHT, IF YOU DON'T WANT YOUR SUPPER, I'LL GIVE IT TO THE CAT NEXT DOOR!

THAT USUALLY DOES IT!
SCHULZ

CHARLIE BROWN I THINK YOU SHOULD RESOLVE TO BE PERFECT DURING THE COMING YEAR...

PERFECT? GOOD GRIEF NOBODY'S PERFECT! WHAT DO YOU EXPECT OF ME?
I THINK YOU CAN BE IF YOU TRY.. I REALLY DO!

ALL RIGHT, LUCY, IF YOU HAVE THAT MUCH FAITH IN ME, I'LL TRY! I HEREBY RESOLVE TO BE PERFECT DURING THE NEXT YEAR!

YOU? PERFECT?!
HA! HA! HA! HA!
SCHULZ

SO YOU REALLY LIKE YOUR TEACHER, EH, LINUS?

SHE'S A GOOD TEACHER, CHARLIE BROWN...NO, SHE'S MORE THAN JUST A GOOD TEACHER..SHE'S A GREAT HUMAN BEING!

NO, SHE'S MORE THAN A GOOD TEACHER AND A GREAT HUMAN BEING...

MISS OTHMAR IS A GOOD TEACHER, A GREAT HUMAN BEING AND A LIVING DOLL!!
SCHULZ

FLOWERS FOR THE TEACHER, EH, LINUS?

YOU'LL NEVER GET ANYWHERE WITH MISS OTHMAR BY USING BRIBERY..

BRIBERY? THIS ISN'T BRIBERY...

I PREFER TO THINK OF IT AS PUMP-PRIMING!
SCHULZ

LINUS SAID THAT MISS OTHMAR REALLY SPOKE OUT AGAINST BLANKETS TODAY...

SHE SAID THAT IF A CHILD DRAGGED A BLANKET AROUND WITH HIM, IT WAS A SIGN OF IMMATURITY, AND SHE SAID THAT SHE WOULD NEVER PUT UP WITH THAT!

WOW!! THAT MEANS HE'S GOING TO HAVE TO CHOOSE BETWEEN HIS BLANKET AND MISS OTHMAR, DOESN'T IT?

WHO'S MISS OTHMAR?
SCHULZ

BUTTERFLIES LIKE ME!
SCHULZ

BOY, I'M GLAD I'M NOT A LIZARD..

YOU HANG AROUND MINDING YOUR OWN BUSINESS WHEN ALL OF A SUDDEN SOME KID COMES ALONG, AND **WHAM!** THERE YOU ARE...

TRAPPED INSIDE A BOTTLE!
SCHULZ

EVERYONE'S SO NERVOUS THESE DAYS..

EVERYONE YOU TALK TO SEEMS TO BE JUMPY..

ISN'T THAT RIGHT, SNOOPY?

AAAUGH!
SCHULZ

I GUESS YOU PLAY ONLY CLASSICAL MUSIC, DON'T YOU, SCHROEDER?

I SUPPOSE YOU WOULDN'T CARE TO PLAY "ROCK-A-BYE, BABY" FOR MY LITTLE SISTER HERE, JUST AS A FAVOR, WOULD YOU?

NO, I WOULDN'T!
I WAS AFRAID OF THAT *SIGH*

BLAAH!
SCHULZ

IT'S A SHAME THAT IT HAS TO SNOW ONLY IN THE WINTER..

IF IT SNOWED IN THE SUMMER, A PERSON COULD STAY OUTSIDE LONGER, AND ENJOY IT MORE...

WELL, I'LL SAY ONE THING FOR YOU...

THE QUALITY OF YOUR STUPIDITY IS RISING!
SCHULZ

THIS, LINUS, IS A PICTURE OF THE HUMAN HEART!

ONE SIDE IS FILLED WITH HATE AND THE OTHER SIDE IS FILLED WITH LOVE...

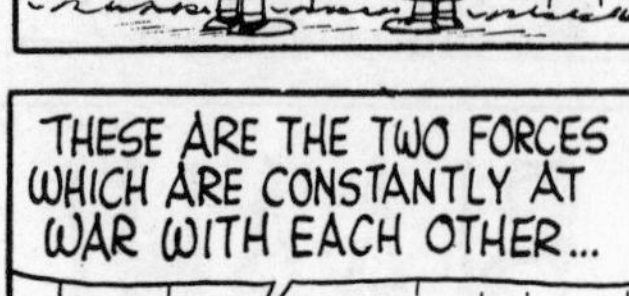
THESE ARE THE TWO FORCES WHICH ARE CONSTANTLY AT WAR WITH EACH OTHER...

I THINK I KNOW JUST WHAT YOU MEAN...I CAN FEEL THEM FIGHTING!
SCHULZ

LUCY SAYS THAT HALF OF OUR HEART IS FILLED WITH HATE AND HALF IS FILLED WITH LOVE...

AND SHE SAYS THIS HATE AND LOVE ARE ALWAYS FIGHTING WITHIN US...ALWAYS QUARRELING, BATTLING, STRUGGLING....

PEACE!
SCHULZ

LUCY, I DON'T **WANT** MY HEART TO BE HALF LOVE AND HALF HATE..

I WANT TO BE ALL LOVE!

GOOD FOR YOU, LINUS...ALL YOU HAVE TO DO IS LEAN A LITTLE TO ONE SIDE....
?

SEE? NOW THE LOVE WILL GET A CHANCE TO SPILL OVER INTO THE HATE!
GOOD GRIEF!
SCHULZ

EVERY NOW AND THEN YOU RUN INTO A KITE WITH A MIND OF ITS OWN!
SCHULZ

I THINK A NICE SMILE ENHANCES ANY PERSONALITY

THAT'S TRUE ...THERE REALLY IS NOTHING MORE ATTRACTIVE THAN A NICE SMILE

WITHIN BOUNDS OF REASON, OF COURSE
OF COURSE
SCHULZ

DO YOU WANT THE REST OF THIS SANDWICH, SNOOPY?

I'VE ALREADY EATEN HALF OF IT.... YOU DON'T MIND?

OKAY, IT'S YOURS..

I'M SO HUMBLE IT'S SICKENING!
SCHULZ

RATS! I FORGOT THE EGG SHELLS!

MISS OTHMAR WANTED US TO BRING SOME EGG SHELLS TO SCHOOL TODAY...WE WERE GOING TO MAKE IGLI...

IGLI?
THAT'S PLURAL, CHARLIE BROWN..

ONE IGLOO...TWO IGLI!
SCHULZ

GOOD GRIEF! I FORGOT THE EGG SHELLS AGAIN!

MISS OTHMAR WILL BE SO UPSET! SHE WANTED US TO BRING EGG SHELLS TO SCHOOL TO MAKE A LITTLE IGLOO VILLAGE...

MISS OTHMAR TAKES HER JOB VERY SERIOUSLY...SHE DOESN'T EVEN LIKE TO BE CALLED A TEACHER...

SHE PREFERS TO BE CALLED AN EDUCATOR!
WOW! HOW SERIOUS CAN YOU GET?
SCHULZ

WELL, DID YOU REMEMBER TO BRING THE EGG SHELLS TODAY, LINUS?

AS SOON AS I WOKE UP THIS MORNING, I THOUGHT TO MYSELF, "HAVE MOM SAVE THE EGG SHELLS WHEN SHE FIXES BREAKFAST!"

SO?

SO TODAY WE HAD COLD CEREAL!
SCHULZ

MISS OTHMAR GOT QUITE UPSET WHEN I TOLD HER I FORGOT THE EGG SHELLS AGAIN TODAY...

SHE TURNED SORT OF PALE AND PUT HER HEAD DOWN ON THE DESK...I THINK SHE MAY EVEN HAVE CRIED A LITTLE...

POOR MISS OTHMAR...I HOPE SHE DOESN'T BECOME ILL...

I NEVER REALIZED IT BEFORE, BUT A SCHOOL TEACHER IS A VERY DELICATE INSTRUMENT!
SCHULZ

..AMEN!

AND PLEASE DON'T LET MISS OTHMAR CRACK UP..
SCHULZ

LOOK, CHARLIE BROWN! I FINALLY REMEMBERED THE EGG SHELLS!

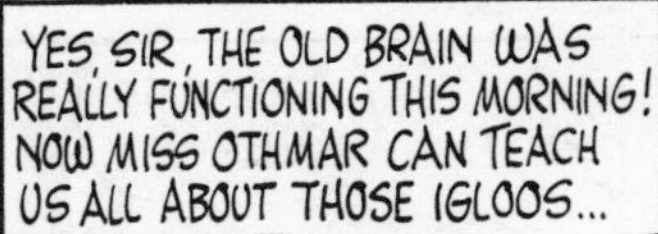
YES, SIR, THE OLD BRAIN WAS REALLY FUNCTIONING THIS MORNING! NOW MISS OTHMAR CAN TEACH US ALL ABOUT THOSE IGLOOS...

SCHULZ
TODAY IS SATURDAY!

WHAT'S THIS ABOUT YOU AND YOUR TEACHER AND SOME EGG SHELLS?

MISS OTHMAR WANTS US TO BRING SOME EGG SHELLS TO SCHOOL TO MAKE IGLOOS, BUT I KEEP FORGETTING...SHE'S VERY UPSET

IT'S JUST LIKE YOU... I'VE NEVER KNOWN ANYONE WHO COULD FORGET THINGS WITH SUCH CLOCKLIKE REGULARITY!

I GUESS I'M JUST MECHANICALLY MINDED!
SCHULZ

POOR MISS OTHMAR..

I HAD TO GO AND FORGET THE EGG SHELLS AGAIN TODAY.. FOR A MINUTE I THOUGHT SHE WAS GOING TO PASS OUT!

SHE WAS REALLY UPSET, HUH?
I'LL SAY!

SHE HAD A PIECE OF CHALK IN HER HAND, AND WHEN IT SNAPPED, IT SOUNDED LIKE A RIFLE SHOT!
SCHULZ

POOR MISS OTHMAR...

SHE'S GETTING MORE NERVOUS EVERY DAY... I THINK SHE HAS TOO MUCH ON HER MIND....

TEACHERS' MEETINGS, REPORTS TO FILL OUT, PLAYGROUND DUTY PARENT-TEACHER CONFERENCES...

..AND EGG SHELLS..
YEAH, AND EGG SHELLS!
SIGH
SCHULZ
2-3

LUCY SAID THAT SHE WOULD SEE TO IT THAT I DON'T FORGET THE EGG SHELLS AGAIN TOMORROW..

IT'S NICE TO BE ABLE TO DOZE OFF FOR A CHANGE WITHOUT ANY WORRIES...IT'S NICE TO KNOW THAT EVERYTHING IS IN GOOD HANDS...

Z

DON'T FORGET THE EGG SHELLS!!

SIGH
SCHULZ

I GUESS I JUST DON'T UNDERSTAND DOGS!
?

I CAN'T IMAGINE WHY THEY WANT AN OLD BARE BONE...

SNOOPY'S HAD **THAT** BONE FOR MONTHS, AND YOU NEVER SEE HIM CHEWING ON IT !!

HAS HE NEVER HEARD OF A CONVERSATION PIECE?
SCHULZ

SCHULZ
SNOOPY
SCHULZ

YOU KNOW WHAT THEY SHOULD DO ON DECEMBER SIXTEENTH?

THEY SHOULD RUN FULL-PAGE ADS IN EVERY NEWSPAPER IN THE COUNTRY WISHING BEETHOVEN A HAPPY BIRTHDAY...

THEY SHOULD HAVE A BIG SPECTACULAR ON TV, AND THEY SHOULD CARVE HIS FACE ON MOUNT RUSHMORE!

THOSE ARE GOOD IDEAS, LUCY...
THANK YOU... WHEN I GET BIG, I'M GOING TO WORK IN AN ADVERTISING AGENCY!
SCHULZ

SCHROEDER, I JUST WANT YOU TO KNOW THAT I'M ON YOUR SIDE!

I'M SURE I CAN HELP YOU PUBLICITYWISE WITH BEETHOVEN'S BIRTHDAY...

AFTER ALL, THIS IS A REALLY BIG THING....

WE MUST DO WHATEVER IS BEST BEETHOVENWISE!
SCHULZ

DID YOU KNOW THAT DECEMBER 16th IS BEETHOVEN'S BIRTHDAY?
NO, I DIDN'T..

WELL, NOW YOU KNOW!
SCHULZ

HEAR YE! HEAR YE!

THE SIXTEENTH OF DECEMBER IS BEETHOVEN'S BIRTHDAY!

HEAR YE! HEAR YE!

SCHULZ

SCHROEDER, YOU'LL BE PROUD OF THE PUBLICITY JOB I'VE DONE!

I'VE TOLD EVERYONE I KNOW ABOUT BEETHOVEN'S BIRTHDAY BEING THIS WEDNESDAY...

JUST THINK, ALL OVER THE COUNTRY PEOPLE WILL BE GATHERED TO RAISE TOASTS, AND SING THEIR BEST WISHES...

"HAPPY BIRTHDAY, KARL BEETHOVEN!!"
OH, NO!
SCHULZ

LOOK, LUCY, PERHAPS YOU SHOULD KNOW THAT BEETHOVEN'S NAME WASN'T KARL... IT WAS....

OH, NOW YOU'RE GOING TO START PICKING ON ME HUH? AFTER ALL I'VE DONE FOR YOU! TRAMPING THE STREETS, RINGING DOORBELLS...

TALKING TO HUNDREDS OF PEOPLE, TELLING THEM ABOUT BEETHOVEN'S BIRTHDAY!

BUT DO I GET THANKED FOR IT? NO! ALL I GET IS CRITICISM!!!
GOOD GRIEF!
SCHULZ

SCHROEDER, I APOLOGIZE FOR THE WAY I FLEW OFF THE HANDLE YESTERDAY..

TO SHOW THAT MY HEART'S IN THE RIGHT PLACE, I'VE COME OVER TO SING "HAPPY BIRTHDAY" TO BEETHOVEN WITH YOU...OKAY?

HAPPY BIRTHDAY TO YOU...
HAPPY BIRTHDAY TO YOU...
HAPPY BIRTHDAY, DEAR LAURENCE....

LAURENCE?
HAPPY BIRTHDAY TO YOOooo!
SCHULZ

OOO, WHAT A FACE!

HE WAS A LOT BETTER LOOKING FROM A DISTANCE!
SCHULZ

GUESS WHAT HAPPENED, CHARLIE BROWN!

I FINALLY REMEMBERED THE EGG SHELLS! I BROUGHT THEM TO SCHOOL, AND GUESS WHAT!

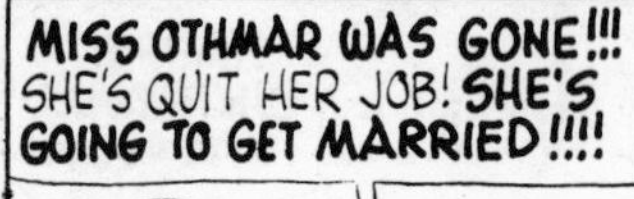
MISS OTHMAR WAS GONE!!! SHE'S QUIT HER JOB! SHE'S GOING TO GET MARRIED!!!!

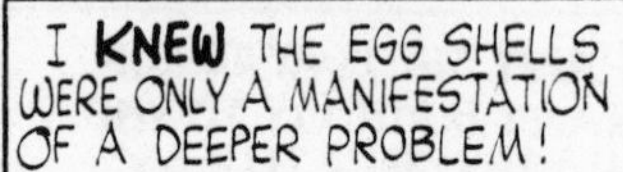
I KNEW THE EGG SHELLS WERE ONLY A MANIFESTATION OF A DEEPER PROBLEM!

SCHULZ

WHAT IN THE WORLD ARE YOU DOING?

I'M GOING TO SEND MISS OTHMAR A WEDDING PRESENT...

WELL, THAT'S VERY THOUGHTFUL OF YOU, LINUS....WHAT ARE YOU SENDING HER?

A BOX OF EGG SHELLS!
SCHULZ

BOY, THIS WEATHER SURE HAS BEEN TERRIBLE!

WHO CAN WALK TO SCHOOL WHEN IT'S THIS COLD? WHO WANTS TO WALK TO SCHOOL ANYWAY? IN FACT, WHO WANTS TO GO TO SCHOOL?

WHO EVER LEARNS ANYTHING? AND WHAT GOOD DOES IT DO YOU? I'M FED UP WITH THE WHOLE WORKS! I HATE EVERYTHING!

TO PUT A LITTLE FUN IN YOUR LIFE, TRY FUSSING!
SCHULZ

HOW LONG DO YOU THINK IT WILL BE BEFORE SALLY STARTS TO WALK?

GOOD GRIEF! WHAT'S THE HURRY? LET HER CRAWL AROUND FOR AWHILE! DON'T RUSH HER!

SHE'S GOT ALL THE TIME IN THE WORLD...

ONCE YOU STAND UP AND START TO WALK, YOU'RE COMMITTED FOR LIFE!
SCHULZ

THAT'S RIDICULOUS!

OH?

WELL, MAYBE SO...

ALL I KNOW IS IT GIVES US A BETTER PICTURE!
SCHULZ

THE PICTURE'S GETTING FUZZY... RAISE YOUR RIGHT EAR..

SIT UP A LITTLE STRAIGHTER.. MAYBE THAT'LL HELP...

MOVE THAT RIGHT EAR SOME MORE, AND LOWER YOUR LEFT EAR...

THERE!! THAT'S FINE! NOW HOLD IT!
SIGH
SCHULZ

BLAH!

MY MOTHER DIDN'T RAISE ME TO BE A TV AERIAL!
SCHULZ

I WOULDN'T MARRY YOU UNLESS YOU WERE THE LAST GIRL ON EARTH!

DID YOU SAY, "IF" OR "UNLESS"?

I ADMIT I SAID, "UNLESS"...

HOPE!
SCHULZ

I'VE MADE SOME LEMONADE, SNOOPY.

I'M GOING TO LET YOU BE THE FIRST ONE TO TASTE IT...

ALL RIGHT, I'LL ADD A LITTLE MORE SUGAR!
SCHULZ

IT'S THE CHILDREN WHO ARE ALWAYS THE VICTIMS OF SIN AND DISHONOR!

WHENEVER SOMETHING GOES WRONG IN THIS WORLD, IT'S WE CHILDREN WHO SUFFER!

YES, AND DOGS, TOO... DOGS ALSO SUFFER!
THANK YOU!
SCHULZ

I'M SURPRISED THERE'S NO REFUND ON THE EMPTY BOTTLES!
SCHULZ

WHEN I GROW UP, I'D LIKE TO STUDY ABOUT PEOPLE...

PEOPLE INTEREST ME... I'D LIKE TO GO TO SOME BIG UNIVERSITY, AND STUDY ALL ABOUT PEOPLE..

I SEE... YOU WANT TO LEARN ABOUT PEOPLE SO THAT WITH YOUR KNOWLEDGE YOU WILL BE EQUIPPED TO HELP THEM...

NO, I'M JUST NOSY!
SCHULZ

WHAT IN THE WORLD ARE YOU DOING?
DON'T YOU KNOW?

THIS IS THE TIME OF YEAR WHEN WE ALL WRITE TO THE "GREAT PUMPKIN," AND TELL HIM WHAT WE WANT FOR HALLOWEEN

THE "GREAT PUMPKIN" LOVES LITTLE CHILDREN

I CAN SEE HIM NOW RISING UP OUT OF THE PUMPKIN PATCH WITH HIS BIG BAG OF TOYS!
SCHULZ

HALLOWEEN'S COMING, CHARLIE BROWN!

I'VE WRITTEN A LETTER TO THE "GREAT PUMPKIN" TELLING HIM WHAT I WANT HIM TO BRING ME...

IF YOU HAVEN'T WRITTEN TO HIM YET, CHARLIE BROWN, YOU'D BETTER HURRY!

OH, I LOVE THIS TIME OF YEAR! EVERYONE'S SO FULL OF JOY AND GOOD WILL!
SCHULZ

WHY DON'T WE GET THE WHOLE GANG TOGETHER, AND GO OUT AND SING PUMPKIN CAROLS?
SCHULZ

...AND THEN ON HALLOWEEN NIGHT THE "GREAT PUMPKIN" RISES UP OUT OF THE PUMPKIN PATCH...

..AND HE BRINGS TOYS TO ALL THE GOOD LITTLE CHILDREN IN THE WORLD!
YOU'RE CRAZY!

ALL RIGHT, SO YOU BELIEVE IN SANTA CLAUS, AND I'LL BELIEVE IN THE "GREAT PUMPKIN"..

THE WAY I SEE IT, IT DOESN'T MATTER WHAT YOU BELIEVE JUST SO YOU'RE SINCERE!
SCHULZ

TOMORROW NIGHT IS OUR BIG NIGHT, LINUS..

ALL YOU HAVE TO DO IS WALK UP TO A HOUSE, RING THE DOORBELL AND SAY, "TRICKS OR TREATS!"

ARE YOU SURE THAT'S LEGAL?
OF COURSE, IT'S LEGAL!

GOOD...I WOULDN'T WANT TO BE ACCUSED OF TAKING PART IN A RUMBLE!
SCHULZ

WELL, WHAT'S THE MATTER WITH **YOU**?

YOU DIDN'T **TELL** ME YOU WERE GOING TO **KILL** IT!
SCHULZ

WELL, HALLOWEEN HAS COME AND GONE...
SO IT HAS
DID THE "GREAT PUMPKIN" BRING YOU LOTS OF NICE PRESENTS?
OH, SHUT UP!
SCHULZ

LOOK AT ME.. I'M THE "GREAT PUMPKIN"!

I RISE UP OUT OF THE PUMPKIN PATCH, AND BRING TOYS TO ALL THE CHILDREN ON HALLOWEEN!

HEY, LINUS! HOW MANY TOYS DID HE BRING YOU?!!
HAHAHAHAHA!!!

I WAS A VICTIM OF FALSE DOCTRINE..
SCHULZ

SIGH

"And so the King was granted his wish..."

"Everything he touched would turn to gold! Now, the next day..."

STOP! YOU DON'T HAVE TO READ ANY FURTHER! I KNOW JUST WHAT'S GOING TO HAPPEN..

THESE THINGS ALWAYS HAVE A WAY OF BACKFIRING!

YOU'RE A FOOL, CHARLIE BROWN!

I DON'T KNOW WHY I WASTE MY TIME EVEN TALKING TO YOU!

AH-
CHOOO!

SCHULZ
I THINK I'M BECOMING ALLERGIC TO CRITICISM!

SCHULZ

SUDDENLY I FEEL LIKE THE PIED PIPER!
SCHULZ

YOU'RE **WEAK**! YOU'RE A REAL **JELLYFISH**!

YOU'RE **DUMB**, YOU'RE **STUPID** YOU'RE **IGNORANT** AND YOU HAVE A **SILLY FACE**!

POOR CHARLIE BROWN... I SEE THE CATS HAVE BEEN USING YOU TO SHARPEN THEIR CLAWS AGAIN, HUH?

YEAH, I'M SORT OF A SPIRITUAL SCRATCHING POST!
SCHULZ

IT'S NICE TO WAKE UP IN THE MORNING WITH A FEELING OF WELL-BEING..

TO KNOW THAT EVEN THOUGH THERE'S SNOW ON THE GROUND AND IT'S A LITTLE CHILLY OUTSIDE, BASICALLY LIFE IS GOOD, AND THAT YOU PERSONALLY ARE...

?
SNOOPY

DOOMED!
SCHULZ

GOOD GRIEF! TRAPPED IN A DOGHOUSE BY AN ICICLE!
SNOOPY

I'LL BET IF I MAKE JUST THE SLIGHTEST MOVE, IT'LL CRASH DOWN, AND KILL ME!

I DON'T WANT TO DIE! I'M TOO **YOUNG** TO DIE! I'M TOO **NICE** TO DIE!

SCHULZ
I'M TOO **ME** TO DIE!!

IT'S SILLY TO BE TRAPPED IN A DOGHOUSE BY AN ICICLE!

I THINK I'LL JUST MAKE A RUN FOR IT! I THINK I'LL JUST ZOOM OUT OF HERE!

I THINK I'LL JUST LEAP UP AND ZOOM RIGHT OUT!

I THINK I'LL JUST LIE HERE FOR THE REST OF MY LIFE!

LOOKS BAD, DOESN'T IT?
TERRIBLE!

YOU KNOW WHAT I'VE HEARD?
NO, WHAT HAVE YOU HEARD?

I'VE HEARD THAT LOUD NOISES WILL SOMETIMES CAUSE AN ICICLE TO FALL...

IS THAT RIGHT?

I'M DOOMED!
SNOOPY

HELLO, HUMANE SOCIETY? WE NEED YOUR ADVICE...HOW DO YOU GET A DOG OUT OF A DOGHOUSE BEFORE AN ICICLE FALLS ON HIM?

HE SAID TO TRY COAXING HIM OUT WITH HIS FAVORITE FOOD... SOMETHING HE JUST CAN'T RESIST...

WHAT'S THE NUMBER OF "VILLELLA'S TAKE-OUT PIZZA PARLOR"?
SCHULZ

I'M DOING JUST WHAT THE MAN FROM THE HUMANE SOCIETY SAID TO DO...

SNIF? SNIF? SNIF?
?
SNOOPY

ZOOM
WHAM!

SAVED BY A PIZZA!
GOOD GRIEF!
SCHULZ

DEAR SANTA CLAUS,

IT HAS COME TO OUR ATTENTION THAT YOU BASE YOUR GIVING ON THE DEPORTMENT OF THE INDIVIDUAL CHILD...

IN OTHER WORDS, YOU JUDGE AS TO WHETHER THE CHILD HAS BEEN GOOD OR BAD...DO YOU REALLY THINK IT IS WISE TO ATTEMPT TO PASS SUCH JUDGMENT?

WHAT IS GOOD? WHAT IS BAD? CAN WE SAY TO OUR NEIGHBOR, "YOU ARE BAD...I AM GOOD"? CAN WE SAY...
OH, BROTHER!
SCHULZ

TO GO FURTHER INTO THIS MATTER OF THE GIFTS YOU BEAR, DEAR SANTA...

IF, PERCHANCE, YOU JUDGE A LITTLE CHILD AS TOO 'BAD' TO RECEIVE ANY TOYS, ARE YOU NOT ALSO JUDGING HIS PARENTS?

AND IF YOU JUDGE THE PARENTS, THEN ARE YOU NOT ALSO JUDGING THE REMAINDER OF THE FAMILY THE INNOCENT BROTHERS OR SISTERS, AS THE CASE MAY BE?

IN OTHER WORDS DEAR SANTA, MUST I SUFFER FOR THE DEEDS OF...
AH, HA!
SCHULZ

I HEARD WHAT YOU WERE SAYING IN THAT LETTER! A FINE BROTHER YOU TURNED OUT TO BE!

LOOK, I WAS ONLY TRYING TO TELL SANTA CLAUS THAT I DIDN'T THINK HE SHOULD PASS UP OUR HOUSE, AND NOT LEAVE ME ANY PRESENTS JUST BECAUSE OF YOU!

IF HE THINKS YOU'VE BEEN BAD ALL YEAR, WHY SHOULD I SUFFER?

DON'T LOOK AT ME...I'M ONLY THE SECRETARY!
SCHULZ

YOU AND YOUR LETTERS TO SANTA CLAUS!

YOU THINK YOU CAN GET ME IN BAD WITH HIM, BUT YOU CAN'T! SANTA IS VERY FORGIVING WITH LITTLE GIRLS!
OH, YEAH?

YEAH! LITTLE GIRLS CAN GET AWAY WITH A LOT MORE THAN LITTLE BOYS!
WHAT MAKES YOU THINK SO?

BECAUSE WE'RE SO CUTE!
SCHULZ

YOU FOOL!

YOU BLOCKHEAD! YOU NITWIT!! YOU NUMSKULL!!!

DO YOU THINK HE HEARD YOU?
I'M SURE HE DID..

INSULTS SEEM TO TRAVEL FARTHER WHEN THE AIR IS THIN!
SCHULZ

cresc.

SCHULZ

SURE, I THINK DOGS SHOULD BE TREATED KINDLY...

I'VE ALWAYS BELIEVED IN BEING KIND TO ANIMALS..

AND I THINK WE SHOULD DO ALL WE CAN TO MAKE OUR PETS HAPPY...
SCHULZ

BUT **THIS** IS RIDICULOUS!!

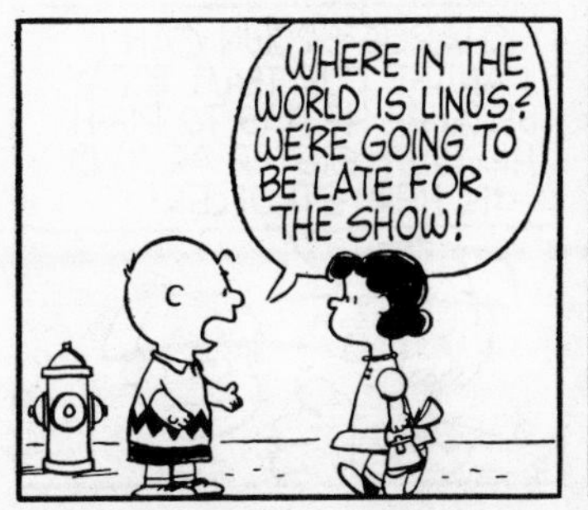
WHERE IN THE WORLD IS LINUS? WE'RE GOING TO BE LATE FOR THE SHOW!

HE BROKE A SHOELACE, AND HAD TO GO BACK TO TRY TO FIND ANOTHER...

I THINK HE'S TAKING ONE OUT OF HIS DAD'S HUNTING BOOTS..

SCHULZ
OKAY, I'M ALL SET TO GO!

THERE'S NO USE ARGUING ABOUT IT! I'D LIKE TO PLAY, BUT I **CAN'T**!

MY MOTHER TOLD ME TO PUSH SALLY AROUND IN HER STROLLER, AND THAT'S WHAT I'M GOING TO DO! IT'S WHAT I **HAVE** TO DO!

WELL, YOU'VE GOT TO ADMIT THAT IT'S THAT KIND OF DEVOTION THAT BUILDS CHARACTER...

...AND **LOSES** BALL GAMES!
SCHULZ

HE WHAT?

CHARLIE BROWN CAN'T MANAGE OUR TEAM TODAY BECAUSE HE HAS TO PUSH HIS BABY SISTER AROUND IN HER STROLLER!

IS THIS **TRUE**?!!

I CAN'T LOOK HIM IN THE EYE!
SCHULZ

I HOPE SHE'S **SATISFIED**!

DEPRIVING US OF A MANAGER JUST BEFORE OUR LAST AND MOST CRUCIAL GAME!

ALL BECAUSE SHE HAS TO RIDE AROUND IN HER OL' STROLLER! **WELL, I JUST HOPE SHE'S SATISFIED!**

MY FIRST YEAR IN THIS WORLD, AND ALREADY I HAVE **GUILT** FEELINGS!
SCHULZ

THERE'S MY BASEBALL TEAM OUT THERE GETTING CLOBBERED..

..AND HERE AM **I**, THEIR MANAGER, FORCED TO WATCH THEM GO DOWN TO DEFEAT BECAUSE I CAN'T PLAY!

AND **WHY** CAN'T I PLAY? **BECAUSE I HAVE TO PUSH MY BABY SISTER AROUND!**

SCHULZ
NOBODY LIKES ME!

HAVE THE INFIELD MOVE IN, AND TRY TO CUT OFF THE RUN AT THE PLATE...

I SHOULD BE BACK HERE IN ABOUT FIVE MINUTES..

GOOD GRIEF!

I'M THE ONLY MANAGER IN THE HISTORY OF THE GAME TO GUIDE HIS TEAM WHILE PUSHING HIS BABY SISTER AROUND THE BLOCK!
SIGH
SCHULZ

WELL, HOW'S THE GAME GOING?

WE'VE STILL GOT A CHANCE, CHARLIE BROWN, BUT WE NEED **YOU**! DON'T YOU THINK YOU'VE PUSHED SALLY LONG ENOUGH?

YOU'RE RIGHT! I'LL RUSH HER HOME, AND ZOOM BACK HERE IN TIME TO **WIN** THE GAME!

DIG OUT, MAN!
SCHULZ

I'M SORRY I CAN'T PUSH YOU ANY MORE, SALLY BUT I HAVE TO GO SAVE MY TEAM FROM DEFEAT

HANG ON, TEAM! HERE COMES YOUR FAITHFUL MANAGER!!

I HAD NO IDEA THAT LIFE WAS GOING TO BE FILLED WITH SUCH DRAMA..
SCHULZ

HERE COMES GOOD OL' CHARLIE BROWN!
HE MUST BE THROUGH PUSHING HIS BABY SISTER!

YOU'RE JUST IN TIME TO GO IN AS A PINCH-HITTER, OL' BUDDY! YOU CAN SAVE THE GAME, OL' PAL!

REMEMBER, OL' BUDDY, WE'RE COUNTING ON YOU!
BE A HERO, CHARLIE BROWN, OL' PAL!

OR DON'T SHOW YOUR FACE AROUND HERE AGAIN!
SCHULZ

IT'S **HERO** TIME!

STRIKE ONE!
GOOD GRIEF!
SCHULZ

THIS IS MY BIG CHANCE TO BE A HERO!

I'M TIRED OF ALWAYS BEING THE GOAT..

EVERYONE HAS THE POTENTIALITIES OF A HERO OR A GOAT LYING WITHIN HIM...

STRIKE TWO!
I CAN FEEL THE **GOAT** IN ME RISING TO THE SURFACE!
SCHULZ

IT ONLY TAKES ONE TO HIT IT.. IT ONLY TAKES ONE TO HIT IT!

THE GAME IS NEVER OVER UNTIL THE LAST MAN IS OUT! I CAN STILL BE A HERO..

IT ONLY TAKES ONE TO HIT IT...

STRIKE THREE!
THAT WASN'T THE ONE!
SCHULZ

I THINK I'M GOING TO CRY..
SCHULZ

WHOEVER TOLD YOU THAT YOU COULD PLAY BASEBALL?! YOU'RE THE WORLD'S WORST! YOU'RE USELESS! YOU'RE TERRIBLE!

SAY, THIS IS WHERE I LIVE..
OH, YES, SO IT IS...

WELL, DON'T WORRY..I'VE STILL GOT A LITTLE WAY TO GO SO I CAN TAKE OVER...

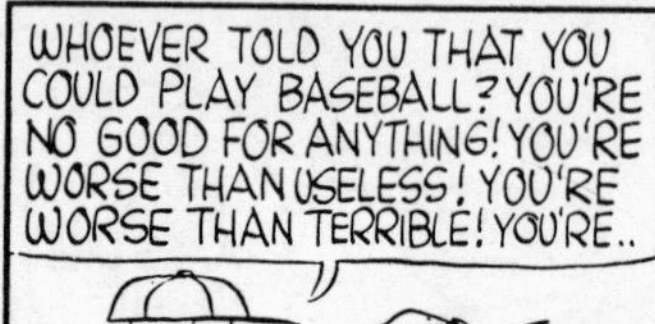

WHOEVER TOLD YOU THAT YOU COULD PLAY BASEBALL? YOU'RE NO GOOD FOR ANYTHING! YOU'RE WORSE THAN USELESS! YOU'RE WORSE THAN TERRIBLE! YOU'RE..
SCHULZ

THIS IS THE WORST YET..I'VE REALLY HIT BOTTOM!

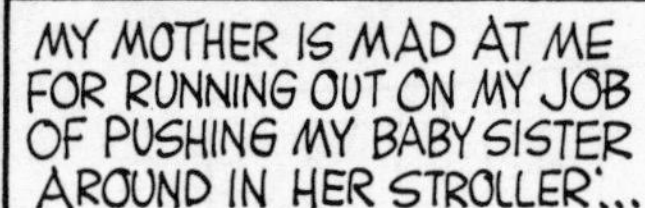

MY MOTHER IS MAD AT ME FOR RUNNING OUT ON MY JOB OF PUSHING MY BABY SISTER AROUND IN HER STROLLER...

AND NOW ALL THE KIDS ARE MAD AT ME FOR STRIKING OUT AND LOSING THE BIGGEST GAME OF THE SEASON!

SUDDENLY I FEEL VERY OLD...
SCHULZ

LIFE IS JUST TOO MUCH FOR ME..

I'VE BEEN CONFUSED RIGHT FROM THE DAY I WAS BORN...

I THINK THE WHOLE TROUBLE IS THAT WE'RE THROWN INTO LIFE TOO FAST...WE'RE NOT REALLY PREPARED...

WHAT DID YOU WANT...A CHANCE TO WARM UP FIRST?
SCHULZ

LOOK, I SACRIFICED A LOT TO COME BACK AND PLAY IN THAT GAME!

I WAS SUPPOSED TO BE PUSHING MY BABY SISTER IN HER STROLLER...NOW MY MOTHER'S MAD AT ME!

BUT I DID IT FOR OUR TEAM! DO YOU UNDERSTAND THAT? I SACRIFICED MYSELF FOR OUR TEAM! **DO** YOU UNDERSTAND THAT, LUCY? **DO YOU?**

I WONDER WHAT BIRDS THINK ABOUT WHEN THEY FLY AROUND UP THERE!
SCHULZ

I'VE BEEN FEELING PRETTY DISCOURAGED THE LAST FEW DAYS, SALLY..

BUT IT'S REALLY ALL MY OWN FAULT...I GUESS I ALSO OWE YOU AN APOLOGY FOR ALL THE COMPLAINING I DID JUST BECAUSE I HAD TO TAKE YOU OUT FOR A WALK

MAYBE IF YOU AND I STICK TOGETHER AS BROTHER AND SISTER WE CAN LICK THIS OLD WORLD YET! WHAT DO YOU SAY?

I'LL DRINK TO THAT!
SCHULZ

DID BEETHOVEN EVER ROLL A "THREE HUNDRED" GAME?

YOU MEAN IN BOWLING? GOOD GRIEF, HOW IN THE WORLD SHOULD I KNOW?!

I THOUGHT YOU WERE AN AUTHORITY ON BEETHOVEN?

SCHULZ

SCHULZ

LOOK, CHARLIE BROWN! A LETTER FROM MISS OTHMAR!

ONLY HER NAME ISN'T OTHMAR ANY MORE...IT'S MRS. HAGEMEYER! SHE THANKS ME FOR THE EGG SHELLS I SENT, AND SAYS SHE'LL KEEP THEM FOREVER...

AND SHE SAYS SHE MISSES ALL THE KIDS IN HER CLASS, BUT YOU KNOW WHO SHE SAYS SHE MISSES MOST? **ME!!**

SCHULZ

ONLY 28 MORE DAYS UNTIL BEETHOVEN'S BIRTHDAY!

WHERE **DOES** THE TIME GO?
SCHULZ

Z

Z

Z

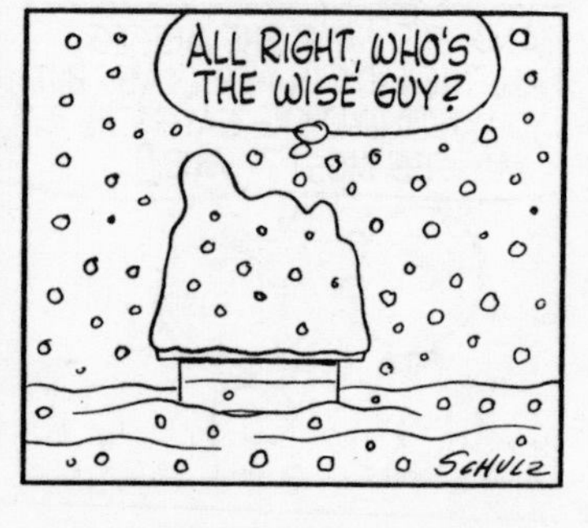
ALL RIGHT, WHO'S THE WISE GUY?
SCHULZ